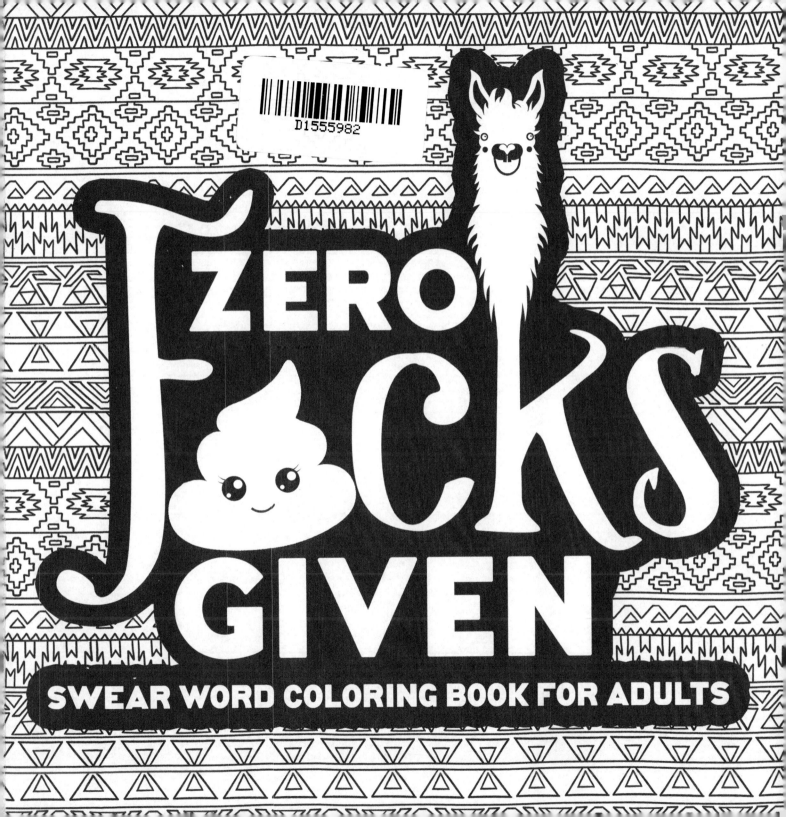

ZERO F*CKS GIVEN

SWEAR WORD COLORING BOOK FOR ADULTS

@honeybadgercoloring

Honey Badger Coloring

Shop our other books at
www.honeybadgercoloring.com

For questions and customer service, email us at
support@honeybadgercoloring.com

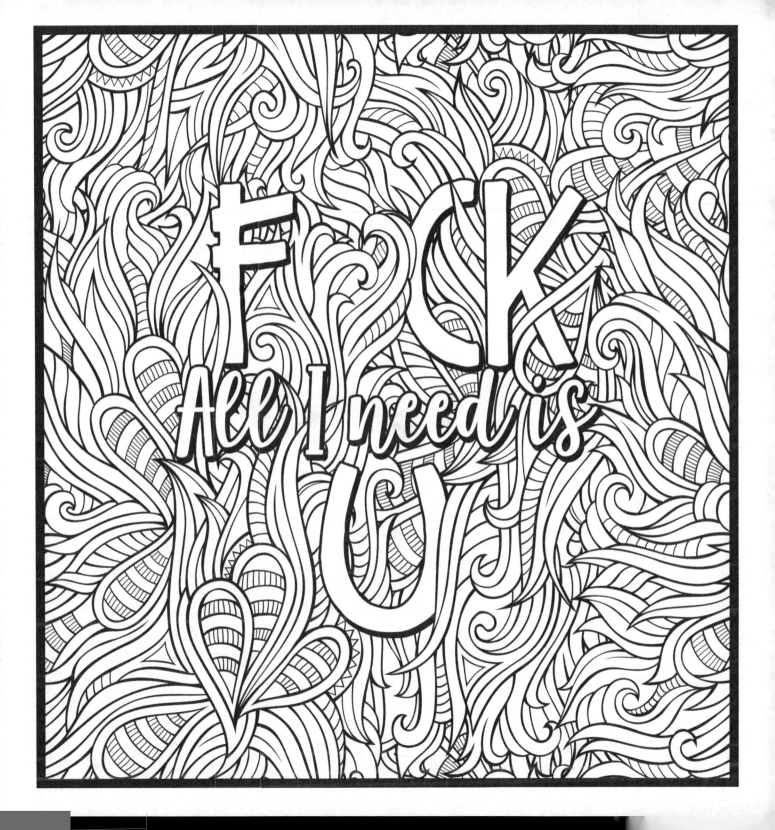

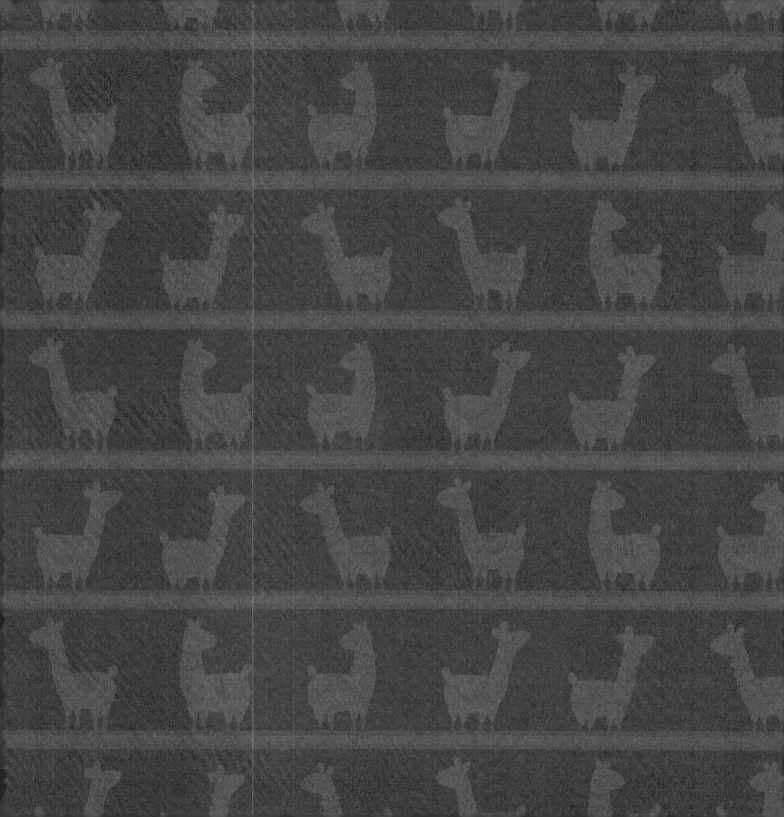

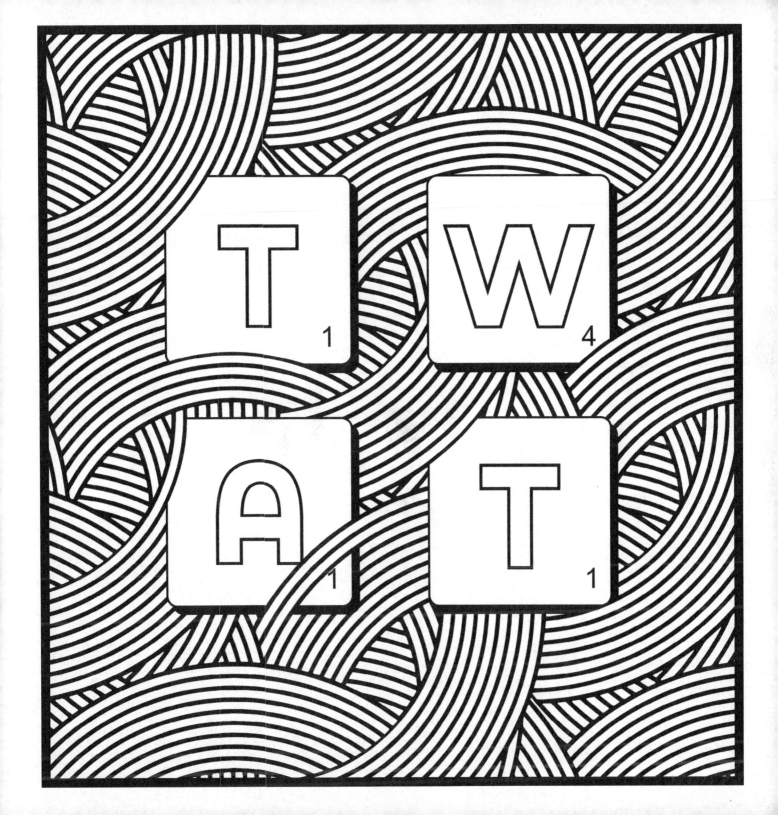

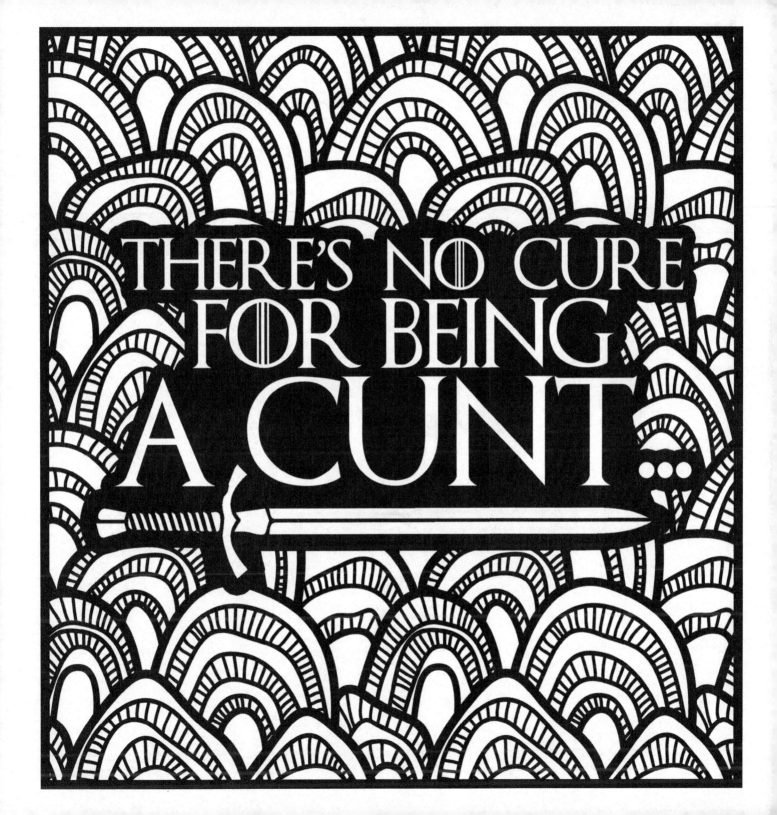

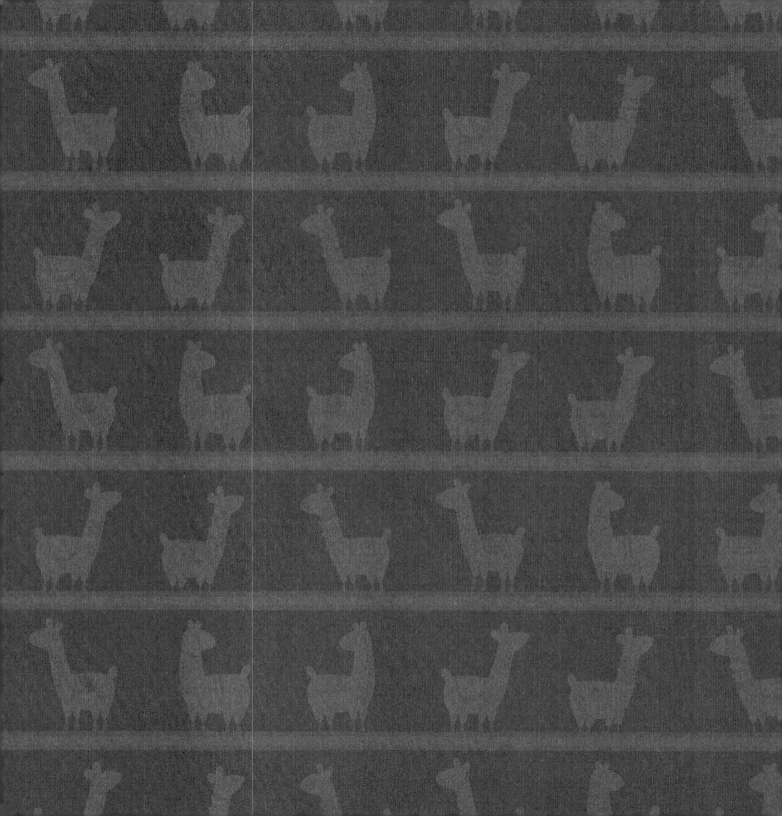

@honeybadgercoloring

Honey Badger Coloring

Shop our other books at
www.honeybadgercoloring.com

For questions and customer service, email us at
support@honeybadgercoloring.com